Grade
7

Name

Date of exam

GW00656602

Contents

Editor for ABRSM: Richard Jones

		page

LIST A

1   **Thomas Augustine Arne** (1710–78) Allegro: second movement from Sonata No. 3 in G — 3

2   **George Frideric Handel** (1685–1759) Allemande: third movement from Suite in D minor, HWV 428 — 6

3   **Wolfgang Amadeus Mozart** (1756–91) Presto: third movement from Sonata in F, K. 280/189e — 8

LIST B

1   **Max Bruch** (1838–1920) Schwedischer Tanz in A minor: No. 14 from *Schwedische Tänze*, Op. 63 — 13

2   **Aleksandr Nikolayevich Skryabin** (1872–1915) Prelude in D flat: No. 3 from Seven Preludes, Op. 17 — 16

3   **Joaquín Turina** (1882–1949) Conchita rêve: No. 6 from *Niñerías*, Series 2, Op. 56 — 18

LIST C

1   **Dmitry Borisovich Kabalevsky** (1904–87) Presto: third movement from Sonatina, Op. 13 No. 1 — 20

2   **Bohuslav Martinů** (1890–1959) Harlequin (Scherzo): from *Puppets*, Book 2 — 25

3   **Paul Francis Webster** (1907–84) **and Sonny Burke** (1914–80) Black Coffee, arr. Frank Booth — 29

Other pieces for this grade

LIST A

4   **C. P. E. Bach** Allegro: 1st movt from Sonata in B flat, Wq. 62/16, H. 116. No. 16 from C. P. E. Bach, *Piano Sonatas*, Vol. 2 (Henle/MDS)

5   **J. S. Bach** Sinfonia No. 10 in G, BWV 796. J. S. Bach, *Inventions and Sinfonias* (ABRSM)

6   **Daquin** Le coucou (The Cuckoo): from *Premier livre de pièces de clavecin*. No. 2 from *A Keyboard Anthology*, 3rd Series, Book 5 (ABRSM)

LIST B

4   **Granados** Viniendo de la fuente (Coming from the Fountain): No. 5 from *Cuentos de la juventud*, Op. 1 (ABRSM) or *More Romantic Pieces for Piano*, Book 4 (ABRSM)

5   **Liszt** Romance in E minor (S. 169). No. 15 from Liszt, *Easy Pieces and Dances* (Bärenreiter)

6   **Szymanowski** Prelude in D flat: No. 3 from Nine Preludes, Op. 1 (Universal/MDS) or *More Romantic Pieces for Piano*, Book 5 (ABRSM)

LIST C

†4   **Gershwin** 'S Wonderful. *Meet George Gershwin at the Keyboard* (Faber)

5   **Stephen Hough** Valse enigmatique No. 2. Hough, *Suite R-B and Other Enigmas* (Weinberger/FM Distribution)

6   **Poulenc** Le petit éléphant: from *L'Histoire de Babar* (piece published separately: Billaudot/UMP)

† This arrangement only

First published in 2010 by ABRSM (Publishing) Ltd, a wholly owned subsidiary of ABRSM, 24 Portland Place, London W1B 1LU, United Kingdom

© 2010 by The Associated Board of the Royal Schools of Music

Unauthorized photocopying is illegal
All rights reserved. No part of this publication may be reproduced, recorded or transmitted in any form or by any means without the prior permission of the copyright owner.

Music origination by Barnes Music Engraving Ltd
Cover by Økvik Design
Printed in England by Headley Brothers Ltd, The Invicta Press, Ashford, Kent

SUTTON MUSIC CENTRE
020 8642 2838

7 95

DO NOT PHOTOCOPY
© MUSIC

Allegro

Second movement from Sonata No. 3 in G

A:1

T. A. Arne

The English musician Thomas Augustine Arne (1710–78) was for many years highly successful as a composer for the London stage. From 1734 he was engaged at the Drury Lane Theatre, for which he continued to produce music until 1775. His genius for melody, which was already recognized in his own time, served him well in his many stage works and song collections. The eight sonatas of 1756 are his only published works for solo keyboard. Dynamics are left to the player's discretion.
Source: *VIII Sonatas or Lessons for the Harpsichord* (London: Walsh, 1756)

© 2010 by The Associated Board of the Royal Schools of Music

DO NOT PHOTOCOPY
© MUSIC

A:2

Allemande

Third movement from Suite in D minor, HWV 428

G. F. Handel

This D minor allemande belongs to the third of the eight suites that Handel published in 1720. The vast majority of his harpsichord works had already been composed by that date, and the 1720 edition represents a carefully planned selection and revision of his best and most mature works for the instrument. The contents are suites only in a loose sense, as they include not only the four traditional French dances – allemande, courante, sarabande and gigue – but also some of the other prominent keyboard genres of the day: fugues, variations, Italianate adagios and allegros, a French *ouverture* and a *passacaille*. Dynamics are left to the player's discretion.
Source: *Suites de pièces pour le clavecin, premier volume* (London, 1720)

© 1991 by The Associated Board of the Royal Schools of Music
Reproduced from *Baroque Keyboard Pieces*, Book IV, edited by Richard Jones (ABRSM)

A:3

Presto

Third movement from Sonata in F, K. 280/189e

W. A. Mozart

DO NOT PHOTOCOPY © MUSIC

Mozart's Sonata in F, K. 280, which ends with this Presto, is the second of a set of six sonatas that he wrote at the age of 19 while in Munich in early 1775. Although the set may have been intended for publication, only one of the six sonatas was printed during Mozart's lifetime. In 1777 he wrote to his father from Augsburg: 'Here and at Munich I have played all my six sonatas [in public] by heart several times.' The F major Presto, according to Denis Matthews (in the performance notes to the ABRSM edition of Mozart's piano sonatas), 'thrives on lightness of texture, thus throwing into relief the mock-fiery outbursts in the development' (bb. 78–106). Grace notes are to be played on the beat.

Source: autograph MS (formerly in the Staatsbibliothek zu Berlin)

© 1978 by The Associated Board of the Royal Schools of Music

Adapted from Mozart: *Sonatas for Pianoforte*, Vol. I, edited by Stanley Sadie (ABRSM)

A LITTLE SLOWER

Blank page

Schwedischer Tanz in A minor

B:1

No. 14 from *Schwedische Tänze*, Op. 63

Max Bruch

Gehend, ruhig bewegt (♩ = 84) [Andante, gently agitated]

The German composer Max Bruch (1838–1920) showed outstanding musical ability as a child, starting to write music at the age of nine. From 1865 to 1870 he held court music directorships at Koblenz and Sondershausen. Then, after a freelance period of about eight years, he held orchestral conducting posts in Berlin, Liverpool and Breslau from 1878 to 1890. In that year he became professor of composition at the Hochschule für Musik in Berlin, rising to assistant director in 1907. The *Schwedische Tänze* (Swedish Dances), Op. 63, are free arrangements by Bruch of traditional Swedish tunes. They were originally published in a version for violin and piano in Berlin in 1892. Players may prefer to perform this piece at a slightly slower tempo of ♩ = c.76.
Source: *Schwedische Tänze*, Op. 63 (Berlin: Simrock, 1892)

© 2010 by The Associated Board of the Royal Schools of Music

DO NOT PHOTOCOPY
© MUSIC

Prelude in D flat

No. 3 from Seven Preludes, Op. 17

A. N. Skryabin

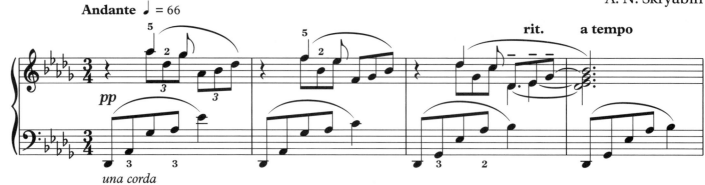

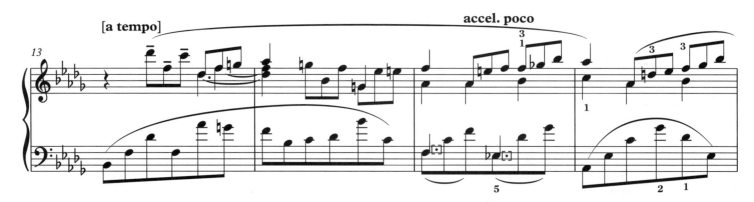

The Russian composer and pianist Aleksandr Nikolayevich Skryabin (1872–1915) studied at the Moscow Conservatory from 1888 to 1892, after which he embarked on a successful career as a concert pianist, playing mainly his own music and that of Chopin. He taught at the Moscow Conservatory from 1898 to 1902 and then moved to Western Europe, not returning to Russia until 1909. His music is written in a very personal and highly chromatic post-Wagnerian style. The Seven Preludes, Op. 17, were composed in 1895–6.

Source: *Sept Préludes pour piano*, Op. 17 (Leipzig: Belaieff, 1897)

© 2010 by The Associated Board of the Royal Schools of Music

B:3

Conchita rêve

No. 6 from *Niñerías*, Series 2, Op. 56

Joaquín Turina

DO NOT PHOTOCOPY
© MUSIC

The Spanish composer Joaquín Turina (1882–1949) studied in his home town of Seville, at the Madrid Conservatory, and then in Paris, where he lived from 1905 to 1914. That year he returned to Madrid, where he was active as a teacher, composer, conductor and critic. Like his compatriots Falla and Albéniz, he incorporated Spanish folk idioms in his music. *Niñerías* (Childish Things) is made up of two suites, the second of which is dedicated to Turina's daughter Conchita. The sixth movement, 'Conchita rêve' (Conchita Dreams), imagines one of her dreams.
Source: *Niñerías, 2me Série*, Op. 56 (Paris: Salabert, 1931)

© by Rouart Lerolle et Cie, 1931

Reproduced by permission of Universal Music Publishing MGB Ltd. All enquiries about this piece, apart from those directly relating to the exams, should be addressed to Universal Music Publishing MGB Ltd, 20 Fulham Broadway, London SW6 1AH.

Presto

Third movement from Sonatina, Op. 13 No. 1

D. B. Kabalevsky

DO NOT PHOTOCOPY
© MUSIC

The Russian composer Dmitry Borisovich Kabalevsky (1904–87) studied piano and composition at the Moscow Conservatory, where he later taught, being appointed professor in 1939. As writer, teacher, composer and administrator, he became a major figure in Soviet music of the 20th century. The first of his two Op. 13 sonatinas, which ends with this Presto, dates from 1930.

© 1994 by Boosey & Hawkes Music Publishers Ltd

Reproduced by permission of the publishers. All enquiries about this piece, apart from those directly relating to the exams, should be addressed to Boosey & Hawkes Music Publishers Ltd, Aldwych House, 71–91 Aldwych, London WC2B 4HN.

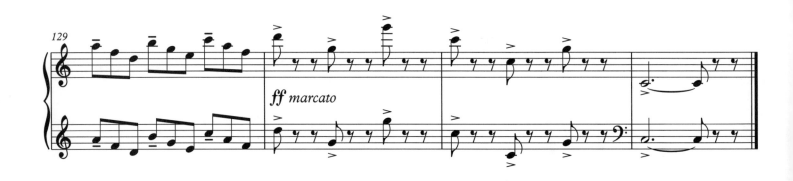

Harlequin
Scherzo
from *Puppets*, Book 2

C:2

Edited by Aleš Březina

Bohuslav Martinů

Bohuslav Martinů (1890–1959) is widely regarded as the most significant Czech composer of the 20th century after Janáček. His three books of short piano pieces entitled *Puppets*, comprising 14 pieces altogether, were composed between 1912 and 1924. They reflect not only Martinů's interest in composing for the stage, but also the established Czech tradition of puppet theatre. Harlequin was a stock comic character in the Italian *commedia dell'arte* of the 16th and 17th centuries. The name now refers to a mute character in pantomime, usually masked and dressed in a diamond-patterned costume. The metronome marks are suggestions for exam purposes.

© 2005 by Editio Bärenreiter Praha
Reproduced by permission of the publishers. All enquiries about this piece, apart from those directly relating to the exams, should be addressed to Bärenreiter Limited, Burnt Mill, Elizabeth Way, Harlow, Essex CM20 2HX.

(Continued on next page)

Black Coffee

Paul Francis Webster
and Sonny Burke

Arranged by Frank Booth

The song *Black Coffee* dates from 1948 and originated in America as the product of a collaboration between lyricist Paul Francis Webster (1907–84) and composer Sonny Burke (1914–80). It was first sung by Sarah Vaughan and later by Peggy Lee and Ella Fitzgerald. More recently it has been recorded by Marianne Faithfull for her 2008 album *Easy Come, Easy Go*. The song is given here in a piano arrangement by Frank Booth.

© Copyright 1948 Webster Music Company/Sondot Music Corporation, USA
Universal Music Publishing Limited (50%)/Chelsea Music Publishing Company Limited (50%)
Used by permission of Chelsea Music Publishing Company Limited, Music Sales Limited and Webster Music Company. All rights reserved. International copyright secured. All enquiries about this piece, apart from those directly relating to the exams, should be addressed to 41GP Music, 41 Great Portland Street, London W1W 7LA.